ACHI BABA
GALLIPOLI 1915

written by Magic Torch
artwork by Andy Lee

Supported by
The National Lottery®
through the Heritage Lottery Fund

heritage
lottery fund

Published by Magic Torch Comics
with assistance from
Heritage Lottery Fund - First World War Then and Now programme

ISBN 978-0-9539065-5-0

Printed by
Comic Printing UK

First Published
June 2015

Researched and written by
Magic Torch

Artwork / colouring / lettering
Andy Lee

Proofread by Wordsmith Jones Editorial Services

Cover font 'Mr Black' and '1913 Typewriter' font licensed from MyFonts

Excerpts from 'The Path of Glory' by George Blake used with the kind permission of the Blake family.

Magic Torch is a Scottish Charity SCO33748

All enquiries auld.dunrod@gmail.com

INTRODUCTION

"When war is declared, truth is the first
casualty." Ponsonby, 'Falsehood in Wartime'

The Gallipoli campaign is famous for many reasons,
and will of course forever be associated with
the Anzacs, interwoven with the beginnings of a
different national identity for Australians and
New Zealanders. However this publication is more
concerned with the attempts on the 'strategically
important' hill of Achi Baba, which involved so
many Inverclyders in the 5th Argyll and Sutherland
Highlanders. It would be difficult to explore and
understand one strand of events in isolation and
so there are references to the wider campaign.

Our projects usually focus on myths and legends,
or the importance of storytelling and so we
were particularly struck by how the campaign at
Gallipoli was so immediately associated with the
epic battles of The Iliad. This was not something
which was retrospectively attached, the generals,
academics and war poets were packaging the campaign
in these classical terms as it unfolded. This is
how many chose to understand and explain the war,
in terms they understood. That was their truth.
There were many others.

We have chosen to explore the story of Achi
Baba through other people's words, including
field reports, letters, poetry and contemporary
articles, some directly related, others with a

less definitive connection. Celebratory jingoism and propaganda sit alongside melancholy or angry personal reflection. For those perhaps unfamiliar with comics and graphic novels, the different voices are represented by a range of different text styles.

This book is not intended as either a military history or a definitive historical account - for as you will see, there is much that is contradictory about these accounts. One thing we can be fairly certain of during wartime, is that the version of the truth that is told depends on who is telling it, and to whom. Definitive truth is so hard to come by, that even the above quotation is claimed by at least half a dozen other originators, starting with the Greek playwright Aesychlus.

In World War One, as in all wars before and since, the one constant reliable truth is that there will be death. And it is to all of those who died as a result of the events detailed within, that we respectfully dedicate this publication.

Paul Bristow
2015

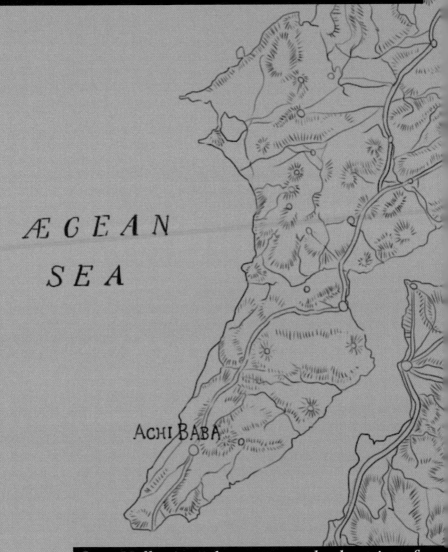

The Gallipoli peninsula in Turkey.
45 miles long and 10 miles at the widest point.
The gateway to Constantinople and the Ottoman Empire.

ÆGEAN

SEA

ACHI BABA

Cape Helles is at the most southerly point of a
largely inhospitable environment, full of ravines
and steep sided hills. There is little water.

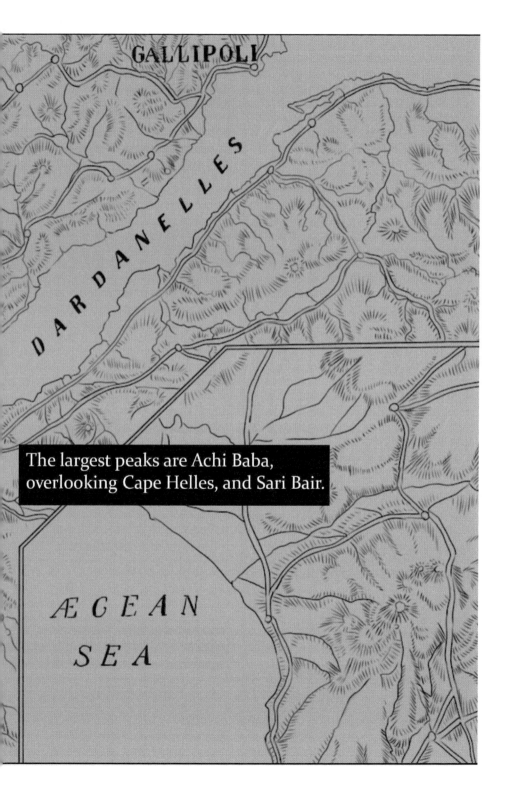

GALLIPOLI

DARDANELLES

The largest peaks are Achi Baba,
overlooking Cape Helles, and Sari Bair.

ÆGEAN

SEA

The Western Front was in deadlock, and the Allied Forces required a new strategy. Winston Churchill, First Lord of the Admiralty, felt that there may be a way to break this deadlock by sea power.
Lord Fisher, the First Sea Lord, was not convinced.

Russia, threatened by Turkey in the Caucasus, had requested aid.

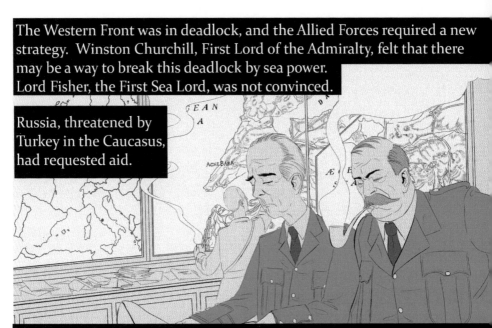

This created an opportunity to open up a 'third front' in the war, stretching the resources of the Central Powers of the German and Austro-Hungarian Empires, and potentially weakening their forces in France and Belgium.

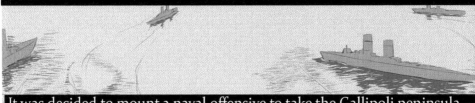

It was decided to mount a naval offensive to take the Gallipoli peninsula – the ultimate objective was Constantinople, capital of the Ottoman Empire.

If Constantinople was captured, the British could create better supply lines with Russia via the Black Sea, force Turkey out of the war and potentially recruit the Balkan states to the Allied cause.

Plans were advanced swiftly. The naval attack began on 19th February 1915.

The British and French Navy bombarded military outposts along the Dardanelles strait in an attempt to push through to Constantinople.

The attacks continued throughout March, with some initial success.

However after three battleships were destroyed, and a further three badly damaged, the operation was abandoned.

Military assistance was requested to continue the campaign, and preparations were made for a series of landings.

Troops committed for the landings were drawn largely from territorial forces, and other regiments untried in battle.

This was not anticipated to be a problem, as Turkish soldiers were believed to be a poor fighting force.

Inverclyde's territorial infantry battallion were the 5th Argylls.
Drawn from towns and villages all across the area, many of them were shipyard workers.

In the early months of the war, the battalion were engaged largely in defence work.

By April, they were mobilised.

The men did not ask whither they were being taken thus.

Perhaps that was a sign of their proper faith in those who led them.

They were going somewhere. Where they were going they would discover in the morning.

In Gallipoli, the first landings were already taking place.

SS River Clyde, built by Russell & Co of Port Glasgow in 1905. The boat was requisitioned by the Admiralty and adapted to be a landing ship for the Gallipoli offensive. She carried 2000 troops, mostly from the Royal Munsters and Royal Dublins.

Holes were cut through the vessel's steel plates to create sally ports which would allow troops to exit quickly. The troops would then use smaller barges as a bridge to reach the shore.

This 'Trojan Horse' was less successful than its predecessor however, and the initial landings at V Beach on 25th April 1915 were a bloodbath.
Troops were mown down by Turkish machine gun fire. Others sank and drowned under the weight of their kit. It was the first of many disastrous mistakes...

April was on the wane, one of the sunniest and most sinister in memory. The transports loomed up at the heel of Gallipoli, the fabulous Hellespont, the scene whence sprung the legend of Leander's daring.

Out of the ships' holds, under cover of naval gunfire, the men swarmed, fired with the spirit of Achilles, the spirit that prefers a glorious short career to undistinguished dotage.

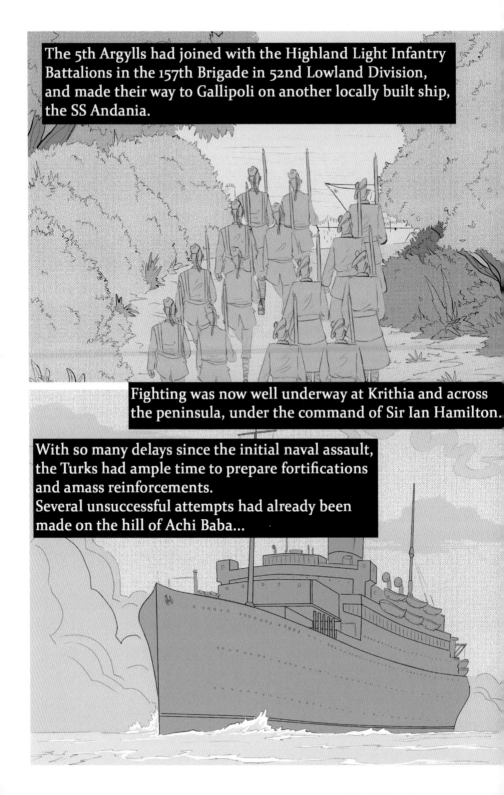

The 5th Argylls had joined with the Highland Light Infantry Battalions in the 157th Brigade in 52nd Lowland Division, and made their way to Gallipoli on another locally built ship, the SS Andania.

Fighting was now well underway at Krithia and across the peninsula, under the command of Sir Ian Hamilton.

With so many delays since the initial naval assault, the Turks had ample time to prepare fortifications and amass reinforcements.
Several unsuccessful attempts had already been made on the hill of Achi Baba...

The dawn had been clear: but presently a curtain of silver, through which gleamed the ghost of the rising sun, hung in ethereal loveliness of texture over the Kereves Dere. This was the smoke of bursting shells.

As the sun mounted higher, all that first mirage of beauty gradually faded. Over the Kereves Dere and beyond, upon Achi Baba himself, what had been a shimmering curtain was now a pall.

Presently that pall was lifted to reveal the monstrous shapes of bursting shells, fierce jism of livid green and black and foul yellow smoke that kept appearing one after another along the Turkish lines

The 5th arrived at Gallipoli on 3rd July 1915. Despite the heavy casualties of previous attempts, General Hunter Weston had convinced Hamilton to attack Achi Baba again.

Place and date having shaped themselves, the intervening period had to be filled in with as much fighting as possible. First, to gain ground; secondly, to maintain the moral ascendency which my troops had by this time established;

thirdly, to keep the enemy's eyes fixed rather upon Helles than Anzac.

Working out my ammunition allowance, I found I could accumulate just enough high explosive shell to enable me to deliver one serious attack per each period of three weeks.

I was thus limited to a single effort on the large scale, plus a prescribed unceasing offensive routine, with bombing, sniping and mining as its methods.

The action of the 12th and 13th of July was meant to be a sequel to the action of the 28th June. That advance had driven back the Turkish right on to just south of Krithia.

The enemy still held their forward system of trenches, and it was my intention on the 12th July to seize the remaining trenches of this foremost system.

On our right the attack was to be entrusted to the French Corps; on the right centre to the 52nd (Lowland) Division. On the 52nd Division's front the operation was planned to take place in two phases: our right was to attack in the morning, our left in the afternoon.

It was coming. Coming. Inexorable.

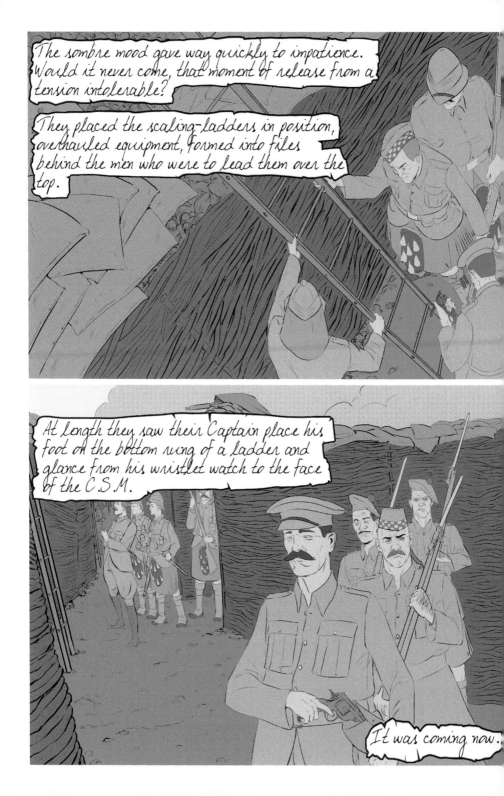

Orders were received that the battalion
would attack in four waves.
The first two waves had orders to jump
over the first two Turkish lines, and
occupy the third.

The Turks were subjected to a heavy bombardment
in the forenoon, and again in the afternoon,
the latter bombardment ceasing about 1 minute
before the time of attack.

At the Hour of attack, 16:50, the men left the trenches
with the 5th Argyll & Sutherland Highlanders on our
left. Our right flank was guarded by the
South Scottish Brigade who had made a successful attack
in the morning.

The men advanced under heavy shrapnel, machine gun, and rifle fire, a number of casualties being sustained.

All three Turkish trenches were taken, but as the third indicated was only a "dummy" the first two waves had to retire, two hours later, into the trench occupied by our third wave.

The critical confusion over the third trench led to many casualties. In the chaos, many Argylls were corralled in a circular stretch of trench referred to as 'the horseshoe', repelling Turkish attack for over 30 hours.

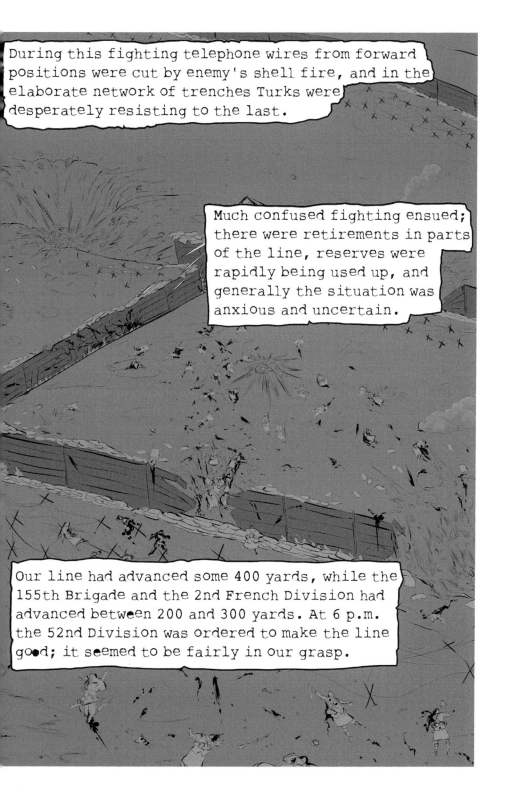

During this fighting telephone wires from forward positions were cut by enemy's shell fire, and in the elaborate network of trenches Turks were desperately resisting to the last.

Much confused fighting ensued; there were retirements in parts of the line, reserves were rapidly being used up, and generally the situation was anxious and uncertain.

Our line had advanced some 400 yards, while the 155th Brigade and the 2nd French Division had advanced between 200 and 300 yards. At 6 p.m. the 52nd Division was ordered to make the line good; it seemed to be fairly in our grasp.

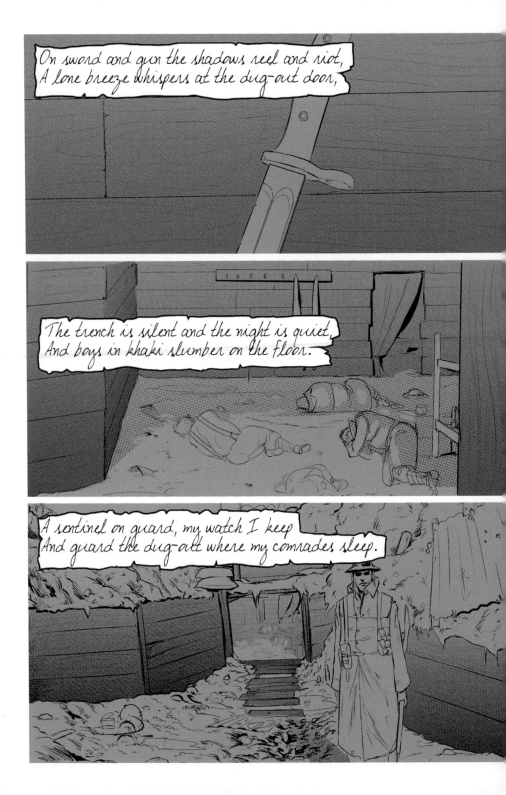

The moon looks down upon a ghost-like figure,
Delving a furrow in the cold, damp sod.

The grave is ready and the lonely digger
Leaves the departed to their rest and God.

I shape a little cross and plant it deep
To mark the dug-out where my comrades sleep.

All night long determined counter-attacks were repulsed but about 7.30 a.m. the right of the 157th Brigade gave way before a party of bombers, and our grip upon the enemy began to weaken.

I therefore decided that three battalions of the Royal Naval Division should reinforce a fresh attack to be made that afternoon, 13th July.

Generally, the upshot of the attack was this. On our right and on the French left two lines had been captured.

Elsewhere a fine feat of arms had been accomplished, and a solid and enduring advance had been achieved, giving us far the best sited line for defence we had hitherto obtained upon the peninsula.

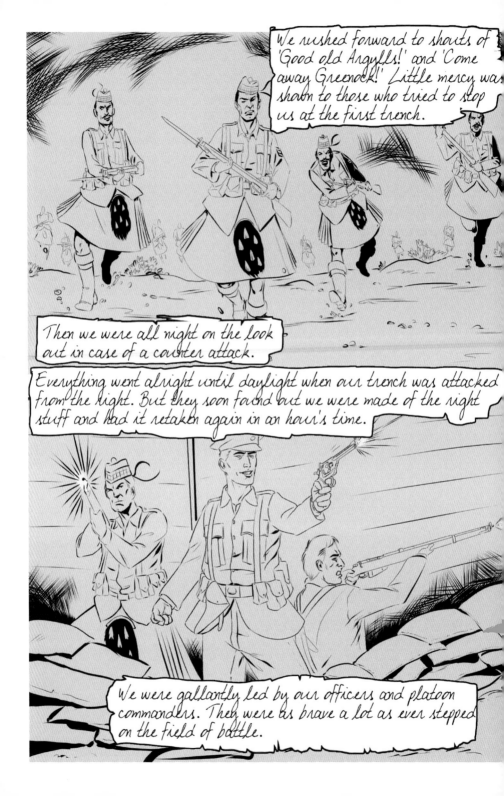

Following the final failed attempt on Achi Baba, the situation on the peninsula settled into a grim deadlock. Requests for reinforcements were not forthcoming.

Meanwhile at home, criticism of the campaign had become political. Lord Fisher demanded an end to it, and resigned when this was overruled, leading to the collapse of the government.

Churchill was relieved of his post, but remained on the War Council, where the campaign continued to be debated for months. And all the while, the troops were trapped in ever worsening conditions...

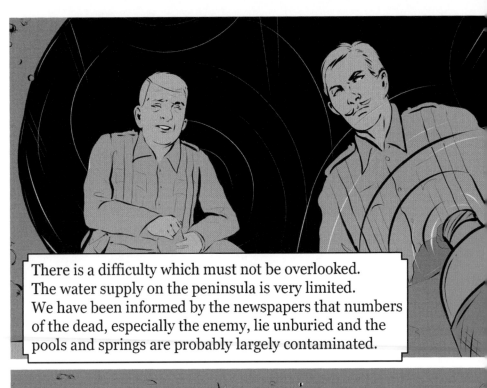

There is a difficulty which must not be overlooked.
The water supply on the peninsula is very limited.
We have been informed by the newspapers that numbers
of the dead, especially the enemy, lie unburied and the
pools and springs are probably largely contaminated.

They were not the houseflies of temperate zones, but coarse brutes with long wings and iridescent bodies of blue and gold.

The soldier learned quickly that the flies which shared his bread and gathered in festering clots in his jam had paddled fhrst in the eyes of dead men and swarmed in the filth of the latrines.

With reference to the climactic conditions in and around the Gallipoli peninsula, somewhat wild statements have appeared in the press. The truth is that the northern end of the Aegean is usually favoured with a delightful winter climate.

With ordinary care, our men have nothing to fear from climactic conditions.

Poor sanitation, the harsh winter storms of October and the blizzards of December, killed thousands.

Sir Ian Hamilton was replaced as commander in October. His successor, Sir Charles Monro recommended an evacuation from Gallipoli. This was finally agreed by the War Committee in December.

The night time evacuation of Allied forces, undertaken over weeks so as not to alert the Turks to a full withdrawal, was perhaps the most successful part of the Gallipoli campaign, with barely any casualties.

Churchill however, was unimpressed by Monro's efforts.

He came. He saw. He capitulated.

This famous hill on one of the greatest of battlefields, Achi Baba, is the natural bastion which defends the road to Constantinople.

Despite the many fierce and valiant attacks by the British and French troops on the hill, the Turks still hold their natural fortress.

Certain critics submit that after the failure of the final attack on May 8th, the whole campaign should have been reconsidered and that the advances made in June and July during which we lost from 30,000 to 40,000 men should never have been attempted.

Following the failure of the Dardanelles and Gallipoli expeditions, the British Government established a panel to prepare a report into the campaign.
Witnesses were interviewed throughout 1916.

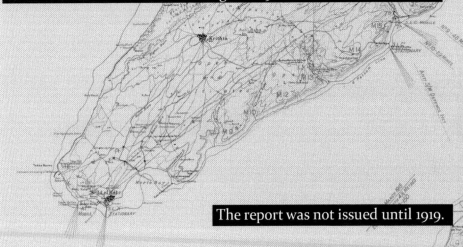

The report was not issued until 1919.

We think that, when it was decided to undertake an important military expedition to the Gallipoli Peninsula, sufficient consideration was not given to the measures necessary to carry out such an expedition with success.

We think that the difficulties of the operations were much underestimated. At the outset all decisions were taken and all provisions based on the assumption that, if a landing were effected, the resistance would be slight and the advance rapid. We can see no sufficient ground for this assumption.

We are of the opinion that, with the resources then available, success in the Dardanelles, if possible, was only possible upon condition that the Government concentrated their efforts upon the enterprise and limited their expenditure of men and material in the Western theatre of war. This condition was never fulfilled.

Many minor frontal attacks were made without adequate artillery preparation, which produced little or no material advantage. Evidence was given that these attacks entailed an unnecessary loss of life.

Without a more intimate knowledge of the locality and conditions than it is possible to obtain, we cannot express an opinion as to whether it was right to undertake such attacks.

In truth the whole episode is tinged with classical romance, spontaneously reviving one's impression of the Iliad. The imagination has already discovered analogy between the wooden horse of Troy and the famous transport River Clyde, which disgorged the fighting men from huge rents in its side.

The very theatre of hostilities itself, was that of the ancient Greeks, for was not Troy situated in the Troad, but two miles from the Hellespont?

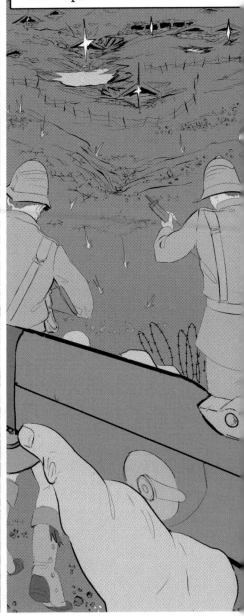

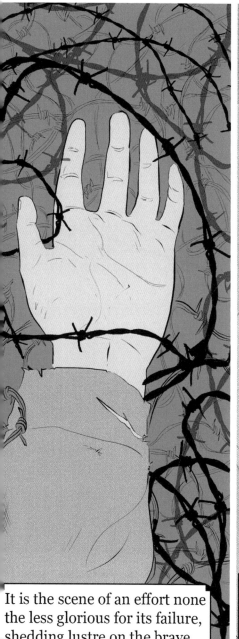

It is the scene of an effort none the less glorious for its failure, shedding lustre on the brave souls who will ever haunt its tortuous ways.

And if mothers, wives and sweethearts have wept for those departed heroes, they, too, must have been thrilled with joy and pride that their men-folk lived and died true to the traditions of a great nation.

250,000 Allied casualties. 50,000 fatalities.

400,000 Turkish and German casualties. 87,000 fatalities.

5th Argylls. 340 casualties. 123 fatalities.

SOURCES

In addition to the research which informed the commentary text throughout, we have directly quoted from a range of sources to create the range of voices we felt were required to tell the story. The source texts are identified below. Many of the documents and materials can also be accessed freely and legitimately online. The Gallipoli campaign is a complex piece of military, social and political history which cannot be easily conveyed in 40 pages. We would suggest interested readers should explore it further.

pg 5 Robert Graves, A Renascence, 1915

pg 11 George Blake, The Path of Glory, 1929

pg 13 War Illustrated, Ghosts of Gallipoli, 29th April 1916

pg15 Compton Mackenzie, Gallipoli Memories,

pg 16, 17 Sir Ian Hamilton, Third Gallipoli Despatch, 1915

pg 18 George Blake, The Path of Glory, 1929

pg 19, 20 Highland Light Infantry, War Diary, 1915

pg 21 Sir Ian Hamilton, Third Gallipoli Despatch, 1915

pg 22, 23 Patrick MacGill, The Night Before and The Night After the Charge, 1917

pg 24 Sir Ian Hamilton, Third Gallipoli Despatch, 1915

pg 25 Compton Mackenzie, Gallipoli Memories

pg 26, 27 Patrick Shaw Stewart, I Saw A Man This Morning, July 1915

pg 28 Greenock Telegraph, A Soldiers Letter Home, August 1915

pg 30,31,33 War Illustrated, In and About Gallipoli, 30th October 1915

pg 34, 35 Dardanelles Commission, 1916-19

pg 36, 37 War Illustrated, Ghosts of Gallipoli, 29th April 1916

pg 38,39 Patrick MacGill (collected) A Soldier Song, 1917

pg 40 Vincent Gillen, Inverclyde's Great War, 2014

RECOMMENDED READING

The Path of Glory
George Blake
Available online via Lulu publications

Inverclyde's Great War
Vincent Gillen
Available online at www.inverclydeww1.org

The texts below are the books and publications we looked to for inspiration in creating a comic set during the First World War.

Charley's War
Pat Mills and Joe Colquhoun
ISBN 978-1840239294

The Great War
Joe Sacco
ISBN 978-0224097710

Above The Dreamless Dead - World War I in Poetry and Comics
Edited by Chris Duffy
ISBN 978-1-62672-065-7

Line of Fire - Diary of an Unknown Soldier
Barroux
ISBN 978-1-907912-39-9

To End All Wars - The Graphic Anthology of The First World War
Edited by Johnathan Clode and John Stuart Clark
ISBN 978-1-908030-13-9
(profits from this publication go to Medecins Sans Frontieres)

The Harlem Hellfighters
Max Brooks and Caanan White
ISBN 978-0-307-46497-2

MAGIC TORCH

Magic Torch is an Inverclyde based cultural enterprise, established in 1999. In that time we have published 8 local books, produced several short films, curated exhibitions across a range of community venues, staged dramatic re-enactments and performances and released two albums of folk tales and folksongs.

Some of our recent projects include

Wee Nasties - A children's picture book and poem which introduces some of the folk characters of Inverclyde to younger audiences.

Tales of the Oak - A vintage terror comic which retells folktales and urban legends from Inverclyde and beyond.

13 Commonwealth Tales - An illustrated storybook featuring Scottish pirate Captain Kidd collecting tales from around the world.

Restorations - A re-edit of the short 1948 film 'Greenock Plans Ahead' with specially commissioned soundtrack by the band British Sea Power.

Copies of our publications can be found online via amazon, ibooks, comixology and scribd.

We also run workshops in 'Community Fables' and comic creation for schools and community groups.

Our ongoing project blog can be found at
www.talesoftheoak.co.uk